jannah bank

Written by
Farida Gessas

Illustrated by
Tamar Blaauw

First published in 2023
Written by Farida Gessas
Illustrated by Tamar Blaauw
Book design by Bryony van der Merwe

ISBN: 978-1-7392034-0-5 (softcover)
ISBN: 978-1-7392034-1-2 (hardcover)

My age

....

My hair colour

....

My eye colour

....

My height

....

I am from

....

I have

....

sisters

I have

....

friends

This book belongs to

....

....

I have

....

brothers

My favourite colour

....

My favourite drink

....

My favourite place

....

My favourite food

....

My favourite surah

....

My favourite hadith

....

Assalaamu alaykum!

So what's the idea behind Jannah Bank?

Jannah Bank diary is all about encouraging you to do at least 10 hasanat (good deeds) each day.

At the end of each day you will find a How Well Did You Do Today page which encourages you to think about the different acts of kindness you did each day.

On this page you get to colour in a gold coin for each hasanah you did. Imagine with each gold coin you colour in, you are collecting and saving them in your bank in Jannah.

Your aim

Your aim is to do 10 hasanat each day so that, insha Allah, you deposit 100 (or more!) in your Jannah Bank.

This is because, out of Allah's kindness, He will generously reward us with 10 times more for each hasanah we do.

How awesome is that!

What to expect...

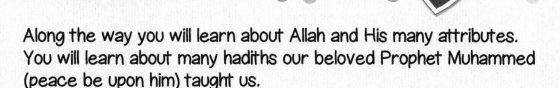

Along the way you will learn about Allah and His many attributes. You will learn about many hadiths our beloved Prophet Muhammed (peace be upon him) taught us.

There are exciting challenges to do. You will find lots of fun activities which will help you to learn more about our beautiful Deen (religion) Islam. Insha Allah you will learn how easy it is to do good and be good.

Important...

Remember though, your actions are based on your niyyah (intention). Make sure your niyyah is to always want to make Allah happy with you.

So, are you excited to fill your 'Jannah Bank' each day with hasanat insha Allah?

Bismillah! Have fun!

Your Aim

To deposit 100 good deeds (hasanat) each day in your Jannah Bank.

How?

Do at least 10 good deeds each day to please Allah!

Remember!

Make your intention (niyyah) to please Allah alone.

JANNAH

ARE YOU READY?

SET?

HAVE FUN!

Here is a list of the many acts of kindness you could do!
Have fun and may Allah reward you abundantly!

Warmly smile at others

Hug your parents

Tell your parents you love them

Ask your parents if they need help with anything and then help them

Help your sister and/or brother

Share with others

Speak kind words about others

Say thank you

Say bismillah before starting anything

Say alhamdulillah for your many blessings

Control your temper when angry

Say astaghfirullah

Complete your salah (prayers)

Read some Quran

Make dua to Allah

Offer to help someone in need

Clear up a mess you didn't make

Eat healthy foods to look after your body

Exercise (run, jump, skip) to look after your body

Can you think of more acts of kindness?

....

....

Did you know?

The Prophet Muhammad (peace be upon him) said: "He who has intended a good deed and has done it, Allah writes it down with Himself as from 10 good deeds to 700 times, or many more times over."

Challenge

Make the niyyah (intention) to do many good deeds at the start of every morning.

Subhan Allah

Allah is Al Wahhab (The Giver of Gifts)

Allah is very generous and has gifted us with many barakat (blessings). Every night Jannah likes to remember her blessings and saying Alhamdulillah before going to sleep.

BARAKA

Colour in the bubble writing.

Write some of the blessings you have.

1 ....

2 ....

3 ....

4 ....

5 ....

6 ....

7 ....

8 ....

9 ....

10 ....

and the list goes on masha Allah

TREASURE HUNT

Remembering the many blessings you are grateful for can help you during hard times. Go on a treasure hunt in your home. Can you find these treasures? Draw a picture of each one.

Colour in the frames.

A food you are grateful for

A person you are grateful for

A toy you are grateful for

You choose something else you are grateful for

A book you are grateful for

You choose something else you are grateful for

HOW WELL DID YOU DO TODAY?

Did you manage to do 10 good deeds? Colour in a gold coin for each good deed you did today. May Allah accept it and reward you 10 times over and more, to deposit in your Jannah Bank.

Let's reflect on how good we were today.

Thoughts and Reflections

What are you grateful for today?

....

....

What made you smile today?

....

....

What will you try to be even better at tomorrow insha Allah?

....

....

DAY 2

Did you know?

The Prophet Muhammad (peace be upon him) said: "Smiling is a charity!" How easy is that? So do a good deed and smile brightly!

Challenge

Count how many people you made smile because of your smile, without telling them!

Allah is Al Karim (The Most Generous)

Draw a picture of someone or something that always makes you smile. Jannah loves to smile to others.

SMILE

Colour in the bubble writing.

Write 10 things you are thankful to Allah for.

1. ....
2. ....
3. ....
4. ....
5. ....
6. ....
7. ....
8. ....
9. ....
10. ....

Take Action!

Can you say "alhamdulillah" 100 times in one minute?

Make a habit of saying "alhamdulillah" 100 times each day.

Alhamdulillah!

Alhamdulillah!

Alhamdulillah!

HOW WELL DID YOU DO TODAY?

Did you manage to do 10 good deeds? Colour in a gold coin for each good deed you did today. May Allah accept it and reward you 10 times over and more, to deposit in your Jannah Bank.

Let's reflect on how good we were today.

Thoughts and Reflections

What are you grateful for today?

....

....

What made you smile today?

....

....

What will you try to be even better at tomorrow insha Allah?

....

....

Did you know?

Allah says in the Quran:
"And the weighing
(of deeds) that Day will be
the truth. So those whose
scales are heavy it is they
who will be the successful."
(7:8)

Challenge

Learn the dhikir
(remembrance) below
because it will weigh heavy on
your good deeds scales insha
Allah.

Allah is Al-'Adl (The Utterly Just)

Allah's Messenger (pbuh) said, that these two duas are easy for the tongue to say and very heavy on the scales (of reward), and most beloved to the Gracious Almighty.

Subhan Allahi wa behamdihi
Subhan Allahil Adhim

Jannah tries to say this dua every morning and evening.

SCALES

Colour in the bubble writing.

BAD

GOOD

Can you say this dhikr 10 times every morning and evening?

DUA TIME

Do you know these duas?
Learn them and say them
when needed.
What to say when...

Going to sleep

اَللّٰهُمَّ بِسْمِكَ أَمُوْتُ وَ أَحْيَ

Bismikal-lahumma amootu wa-ahya

O Allah, with Your name I die and live

I wake up

الْحَمْدُ للهِ الَّذِي أَحْيَانَا بَعْدَ مَا أَمَاتَنَا وَإِلَيْهِ النُّشُورُ

Alhamdu lillaahil-lathee 'ahyaanaa ba'da maa 'amaatanaa wa'ilayhin-nushoor

Praise is to Allah Who gives us life after He has caused us to die
and to Him is the return

I meet a Muslim

اَلسَّلاَ مُ عَلَيْكُمْ

As-salam alaykum

Peace be upon you

Responding to the Muslim greeting

وَعَلَيْكُمُ اَلسَّلَامُ

Wa alaikum as-salam

May peace be upon you

I am about to eat

بِسْمِ اللهِ الرَّحْمٰنِ الرَّحِيْمِ

Bismillah-Hir-Rahman-Nir-Rahim

In the Name of Allah, the most Beneficent, and the most Merciful

I finish eating

الْحَمْدُ لله الَّذِي أَطْعَمَنَا، وَسَقَانَا، وَجَعَلَنَا مُسْلِمِينَ

Alhamdulilahil ladhee at'amana, wasaqana, waja'alana Muslimeen

All Praise be to Allah Who has fed us and given us drink
and made us Muslims

HOW WELL DID YOU DO TODAY?

Did you manage to do 10 good deeds? Colour in a gold coin for each good deed you did today. May Allah accept it and reward you 10 times over and more, to deposit in your Jannah Bank.

Let's reflect on how good we were today.

Thoughts and Reflections

What are you grateful for today?

....

....

What made you smile today?

....

....

What will you try to be even better at tomorrow insha Allah?

....

....

DAY 4

Did you know?

The Prophet Muhammad (peace be upon him) said: "Allah will reward you 10 times for every letter you read from the Quran."

Challenge

Read a verse from the Quran. How many letters have you read? Say Alhamdulillah.

Allah is An-Nur (The Light)

Jannah loves to read the Quran with her family and learn new surahs.

Colour in the bubble writing.

QURAN

Write the names of your favourite surahs or ayahs.

....

....

....

....

....

MAZE RUNNER

Can you help Jannah get to the Masjid?

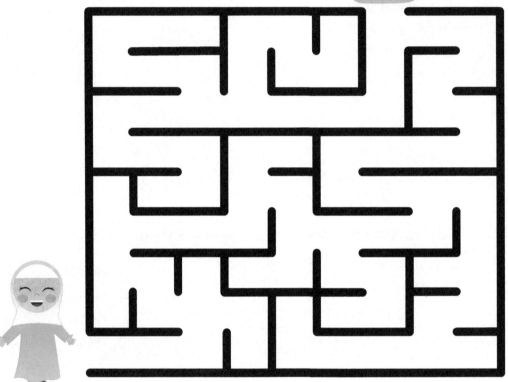

Take Action!

Can you find out what this jumbled up word is
in less than one minute?
Ready? Set? Go!

SCEUSCS

HOW WELL DID YOU DO TODAY?

Did you manage to do 10 good deeds? Colour in a gold coin for each good deed you did today.
May Allah accept it and reward you 10 times over and more, to deposit in your Jannah Bank.

Thoughts and Reflections

What are you grateful for today?

....

....

What made you smile today?

....

....

What will you try to be even better at tomorrow insha Allah?

....

....

Did you know?

Allah says in the Quran:
"Remember Me and I will remember you." (2:152)

Challenge

What is the name of the surah in 2:152?

Allah is Ash-Shaheed
(The All and Ever Witnessing)

The Quran is grouped into 30 juz or parts. Each juz contains surahs (chapters). There are 114 surahs all together in the Quran, with each surah containing a different number of ayat (verses).
Jannah loves this verse in the Quran:

2 : 152

surah number ⟶ [   ]   [   ] ⟵ ayah number

Colour in the bubble writing.

Can you find the answers?

What is the surah number for the chapter name Al-Hadid? ....

How many ayat are there in the surah Al-Hijr? ....

How many ayat are there in surah number 103? ....

Write 6 dream duas you want to ask Allah for everyday.

1. ....

2. ....

3. ....

4. ....

5. ....

6. ....

Here are some good times during the day to make dua (supplication).

In sujood (prostration)

After finishing salah (prayer)

Right after wudu (ablution)

Friday afternoon after Asr

Take Action!

Choose a time to make dua everyday and ask Allah for all your 6 dream duas.

HOW WELL DID YOU DO TODAY?

Did you manage to do 10 good deeds? Colour in a gold coin for each good deed you did today. May Allah accept it and reward you 10 times over and more, to deposit in your Jannah Bank.

Let's reflect on how good we were today.

① ② ③ ④ ⑤
⑥ ⑦ ⑧ ⑨ ⑩

Thoughts and Reflections

What are you grateful for today?

....

....

What made you smile today?

....

....

What will you try to be even better at tomorrow insha Allah?

....

....

Challenge

Hug your parents and tell them that you love them. Ask them if you can help them with something.

Did you know?

Allah says in the Quran:
"... and be good to your parents."
(6:151)

Allah is Al-Bar
(The Source of Goodness, the Kind Benefactor)

Draw a picture of an activity you enjoy doing with your parents. Jannah loves to bake cupcakes with her family.

PARENTS

Colour in the bubble writing.

Jannah is thinking of different ways to keep her parents happy with her. Help her write down what she could do in the hearts.

HOW WELL DID YOU DO TODAY?

Did you manage to do 10 good deeds? Colour in a gold coin for each good deed you did today. May Allah accept it and reward you 10 times over and more, to deposit in your Jannah Bank.

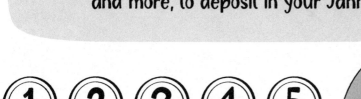

Let's reflect on how good we were today.

Thoughts and Reflections

What are you grateful for today?

....
....

What made you smile today?

....
....

What will you try to be even better at tomorrow insha Allah?

....
....

Did you know?

Allah says in the Quran:
"...and do good, for Allah loves those who do good."
(2:195)

Challenge

Make the niyyah (intention) that you will do your school work with ihsan (excellence) every day.

I make the niyyah to always help my friends with ihsan.

I make the intention to always help out in the masjid with ihsan.

**Allah is Al-Maajid
(The Illustrious, The Magnificent)**

Write a list of three things that you will make a habit of doing with ihsan (excellence). Jannah makes the niyyah every morning that she will do her best in school.

IHSAN

Colour in the bubble writing.

Three things I will do with ihsan

1 ....

2 ....

3 ....

DO YOUR BEST

Sometimes it is tough being a kid. You may have responsibilities at home, school or even at your local masjid (mosque).

Write the responsibilities you have in the boxes, and give yourself a mark out of 10 (10 being the highest) on how good you are at doing it. Allah tells us to work with ihsan (excellence), so do YOUR best.

	/10		/10
	/10		/10
	/10		/10

HOW WELL DID YOU DO TODAY?

Did you manage to do 10 good deeds? Colour in a gold coin for each good deed you did today. May Allah accept it and reward you 10 times over and more, to deposit in your Jannah Bank.

Let's reflect on how good we were today.

Thoughts and Reflections

What are you grateful for today?

....

....

What made you smile today?

....

....

What will you try to be even better at tomorrow insha Allah?

....

....

Did you know?

The Prophet Muhammad (peace be upon him) said: "When a believer does a sin (a bad deed), a black spot appears on his heart. If he repents and gives up that sin and seeks forgiveness, his heart will be polished."

Challenge

Can you say 100 astaghfirullah in under one minute? Ready? Set? Go!

Allah is Al-Ghafoor (The All-Forgiving)

Allah loves those who purify their hearts by turning to Him and really asking Him for forgiveness. The best dua for istighfaar is the one below. Jannah likes to say this dua once every morning and evening.

SAYYIDUL ISTIGHFAR

Best dua for Asking for Allah's Forgiveness

اَللّٰهُمَّ أَنْتَ رَبِّيْ لَا اِلٰهَ اِلَّا أَنْتَ خَلَقْتَنِيْ وَأَنَا عَبْدُكَ وَأَنَا عَلٰى عَهْدِكَ وَوَعْدِكَ مَا اسْتَطَعْتُ أَعُوْذُ بِكَ مِنْ شَرِّ مَا صَنَعْتُ أَبُوءُ لَكَ بِنِعْمَتِكَ عَلَيَّ وَأَبُوءُ بِذَنْبِيْ فَاغْفِرْ لِيْ ذُنُوْبِىْ فَإِنَّه لَا يَغْفِرُ الذُّنُوْبَ إِلَّا أَنْتَ

Allahumma anta Rabbii laa ilaaha illaa anta, Khalaq-tanii wa ana 'Abduka, wa ana a'la a'hdika wa wa'dika mastata'tu, a'udhu bika min sharri maa sana'tu, abuo-u laka bini'matika a'laiya, wa abuo-u laka bidhanbii faghfirli, fa innahuo laa yaghfiru-dhunouba illaa anta.

O Allah, You are my Lord; there is no god except You. You created me and I am Your servant. And I abide by Your oath and promise [that I may honour it] to the best of my ability. I seek refuge with You from every evil I have committed. I acknowledge Your favour upon me and I acknowledge my sin, so forgive me, for surely there is no one who can forgive sins except You.

How to keep a
Beautiful Heart

♡ Say many astaghfirullah during the day and night.

♥ Give charity. You can give food, your time to help someone, or a toy.

♡ Be kind and polite to others.

♡ Make dua to Allah to keep your heart beautiful.

♡ Remember all the lovely things that you have and say alhamdulillah.

♥ Forgive others and don't hold grudges. That's not healthy.

♡ Think good of others.

♥ Do lots of small (and big!) acts of kindness.

♡ Read Quran. The words of Allah are healing to the heart.

HOW WELL DID YOU DO TODAY?

Did you manage to do 10 good deeds? Colour in a gold coin for each good deed you did today.
May Allah accept it and reward you 10 times over and more, to deposit in your Jannah Bank.

Let's reflect on how good we were today.

Thoughts and Reflections

What are you grateful for today?

....

....

What made you smile today?

....

....

What will you try to be even better at tomorrow insha Allah?

....

....

Did you know?

The Prophet Muhammad (peace be upon him) said: "Allah created mercy in 100 parts and He kept with Him 99 parts, and He sent down one part to earth. From that one part the creation is merciful to each other, such that a horse raises it's hoof over it's child out of fear of trampling it."

Challenge

Remember Allah and choose a dhikr to say 100 times.

Allah is Al-Rahman (The Most Merciful)

Allah loves when we show mercy to others. Write 5 ways you show mercy. Jannah is kind to her family, including their kitten.

MERCY

Colour in the bubble writing.

1 ....

2 ....

3 ....

4 ....

5 ....

YOUR HEART IS KING!

Imagine a beautiful land full of your favourite fruits. You would want it to stay beautiful.

Your heart is like that beautiful land.

Keep it beautiful by doing things that please Allah. Do a good deed now.

I am going to hug my parents and tell them I love them.

I'm going to say astaghfirullah 100 times.

I am going to make dua for all the ummah.

I'm going to share my toys.

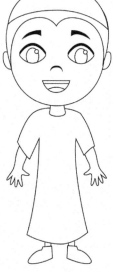

Colour in the children in your favourite colours.

HOW WELL DID YOU DO TODAY?

Did you manage to do 10 good deeds? Colour in a gold coin for each good deed you did today. May Allah accept it and reward you 10 times over and more, to deposit in your Jannah Bank.

Let's reflect on how good we were today.

Thoughts and Reflections

What are you grateful for today?

....

....

What made you smile today?

....

....

What will you try to be even better at tomorrow insha Allah?

....

....

Did you know?

The Prophet Muhammad (peace be upon him) said: "Allah is Beautiful and loves beauty."

Challenge

Next time you see one of Allah's beautiful creations say Subhan Allah.

Allah is Al-Khaliq (The Creator)

Allah created you in the best form (95:4). Next time you look at yourself in the mirror, say the dua (supplication) below. Jannah likes to ask Allah to beautify her manners.

Colour in the bubble writing.

BEAUTIFUL

اللهُمَّ كمَا حسَّنْتَ خلْقِي فحَسِّنْ خُلُقِي

Allahumma kamaa hassanta kholqii fahassin khuluqii

Oh Allah, please beautify my character as how you have beautified me.

DUA TIME

Do you know these duas?
Learn them and say them
when needed.
What to say when...

When entering the toilet

اللَّهُمَّ إِنِّي أَعُوذُ بِكَ مِنَ الْخُبْثِ وَالْخَبَائِثِ

Allahumma innee aoothu bika minal-khubthi wal-khaba-ith

O Allah, I take refuge with you from all evil and evil-doers

When leaving the toilet

غُفْرَانَكَ

Ghufranak

O Allah. I seek your forgiveness

When leaving home

بِسْمِ اللهِ تَوَكَّلْتُ عَلَى اللهِ، وَلاَ حَوْلَ وَلاَ قُوَّةَ إِلاَّ بِاللهِ

Bismil-lah, tawakkaltu alal-lah, wala hawla wala quwwata illa billah

In the name of Allah, I place my trust in Allah, and there is no might nor
power except with Allah

When entering home

بِسْمِ اللهِ وَلَجْنَا، وَ بِسْمِ اللهِ خَرَجْنَا، وَعَلَى رَبِّنَا تَوَكَّلْنَا

Bismillaahi walajnaa, wa bismillaahi kharajnaa, wa alaaRabbinaa tawakkalnaa

In the Name of Allah we enter, in the Name of Allah we leave,
and upon our Lord we depend

When boarding a car or other transport

الْحَمْدُ لِلهِ ، سُبْحَانَ الَّذِي سَخَّرَ لَنَا هَذَا وَمَا كُنَّا لَهُ مُقْرِنِينَ ، وَإِنَّا إِلَى رَبِّنَا لَمُنْقَلِبُونَ بِسْمِ الله

Bismillah, Al-ḥamdu lillah, subḥaan-allathee sakhkhara lanaa haathaa wa maa
kunnaa lahu muqrineen, wa innaa ilaa rabbinaa la munqaliboon

In the name of Allah, All praise be to Allah, Glory be Him who has caused this
(transport) to be under our control though we were unable to control it. And
surely we will return to our Lord

HOW WELL DID YOU DO TODAY?

Did you manage to do 10 good deeds? Colour in a gold coin for each good deed you did today. May Allah accept it and reward you 10 times over and more, to deposit in your Jannah Bank.

Let's reflect on how good we were today.

Thoughts and Reflections

What are you grateful for today?

....

....

What made you smile today?

....

....

What will you try to be even better at tomorrow insha Allah?

....

....

Did you know?

Allah says in the Quran: "Verily, in the remembrance of Allah do hearts find rest." (13:28)

Challenge

Next time you may feel sad, do lots of dhikr (remembrance) of Allah.

Subhan Allah

Allahu Akbar

Alhamdullilah

Alhamdullilah

Allah is As-Salam (The Giver of Peace)

How will you remember Allah today? Which dhikr (remembrance) will you choose to say today? Write it in the box below. Jannah loves to say alhamdulillah.

PEACE

Colour in the bubble writing.

THINGS TO DO WHEN YOU'RE FEELING BLUE

Say astaghfirullah many times.

Talk to Allah through the day and tell Him how you feel.

Talk to a good friend and share how you feel.

Think of all the blessings you have and say alhamdullilah!

Help someone else. Helping others helps us feel better.

HOW WELL DID YOU DO TODAY?

Did you manage to do 10 good deeds? Colour in a gold coin for each good deed you did today. May Allah accept it and reward you 10 times over and more, to deposit in your Jannah Bank.

Let's reflect on how good we were today.

Thoughts and Reflections

What are you grateful for today?

....

....

What made you smile today?

....

....

What will you try to be even better at tomorrow insha Allah?

....

....

Did you know?

The Prophet Muhammad (peace be upon him) said: "The nearest a servant comes to his Lord is in sujood (prostration), so make dua (supplication)."

Challenge

Next time you do your salah (prayer), make dua in sujood.

6 dream duas

1 _____
2 _____
3 _____
4 _____
5 _____
6 _____

Allah is Al-Mujeeb (The Responsive)

Write a list of 3 things you would like to ask Allah for in sujood. Jannah likes to make her 6 dream duas in sujood.

Colour in the bubble writing.

SUJOOD

1 ....

2 ....

3 ....

Jannah is thinking of the many blessings she has that make her happy. Write down the blessings you have that make you happy.

HOW WELL DID YOU DO TODAY?

Did you manage to do 10 good deeds? Colour in a gold coin for each good deed you did today. May Allah accept it and reward you 10 times over and more, to deposit in your Jannah Bank.

Let's reflect on how good we were today.

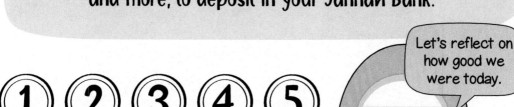

Thoughts and Reflections

What are you grateful for today?

....

....

What made you smile today?

....

....

What will you try to be even better at tomorrow insha Allah?

....

....

Did you know?

There are 25 prophets mentioned in the Quran.

Challenge

Can you name ten of the prophets mentioned in the Quran?

Allah is Al-Azeez (The All Mighty)

Can you unscramble the names of the prophets? Jannah loves to listen to her mother reading the stories of the prophets.

PROPHETS

Colour in the bubble writing.

braIhim ⟶ ....

aIs ⟶ ....

uhaMmed ⟶ ....

suaM ⟶ ....

fusuY ⟶ ....

PEACEFUL PROPHETS

Can you match the prophet to their book?
One has been done for you.

Prophet Dawud
(peace be upon him)

Prophet Ibrahim
(peace be upon him)

Prophet Musa
(peace be upon him)

Prophet Isa
(peace be upon him)

Prophet Muhammad
(peace be upon him)

Scrolls

Gospel

Torah

Quran

Psalms

HOW WELL DID YOU DO TODAY?

Did you manage to do 10 good deeds? Colour in a gold coin for each good deed you did today. May Allah accept it and reward you 10 times over and more, to deposit in your Jannah Bank.

Let's reflect on how good we were today.

Thoughts and Reflections

What are you grateful for today?

....

....

What made you smile today?

....

....

What will you try to be even better at tomorrow insha Allah?

....

....

DAY 14

Did you know?

Allah says in the Quran:
"Remember me. I will remember you."
(2:152)

Challenge

Say the dua
Subhan Allah wa bi hamdihi
Subhan Allah Al atheem
100 times today.

Allah is As-Samee (The All-Hearing)

Allah is Al-Samee and can hear your prayers. Allah is so beautiful that He will remember you when you remember Him. Make sure you remember Him in good times and hard times. Write the times you remembered Allah today. Jannah likes to say the morning dua when she first gets up.

Colour in the bubble writing.

DHIKR

1 I remembered Allah when I woke up with dua.

2

3

4

5

CHALLENGING CROSSWORDS

Can you complete the crossword? Use these names to help you.

Musa Sulaiman Nuh Isa Yaqub Ayyub Yunus
Yusuf Muhammed Ismail Adam Ibrahim

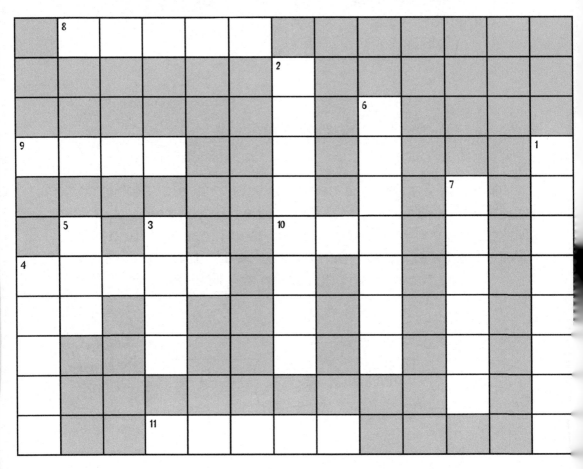

Down ↓

1. The last prophet
2. Can speak to animals
3. His stick turned into a snake
4. Was swallowed by a whale
5. His people were drowned
6. Built the Kaaba
7. Helped his father build the Kaaba

Across →

4. Was thrown in the well
8. Yusuf's father
9. The first prophet
10. Was raised to the heavens
11. Was tested through illness

HOW WELL DID YOU DO TODAY?

Did you manage to do 10 good deeds? Colour in a gold coin for each good deed you did today. May Allah accept it and reward you 10 times over and more, to deposit in your Jannah Bank.

Let's reflect on how good we were today.

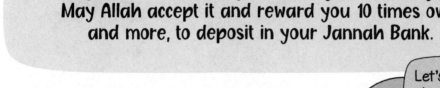

Thoughts and Reflections

What are you grateful for today?

....

....

What made you smile today?

....

....

What will you try to be even better at tomorrow insha Allah?

....

....

DAY 15

Did you know?

Allah says in the Quran that He will not change the condition of the people until they change what is within themselves.
(13:11)

Challenge

Next time you're feeling stuck, get up and change your state and do an act of kindness.

I will do 50 star jumps each day.

I will eat 3 dates each day.

Allah is Al-Jabbar
(The Compeller, The Restorer)

The Prophets are great examples of thinking positively and taking positive action. Which positive action will you make a habit of doing every day? Jannah feels good when she plays and races her friends.

ACTION

Colour in the bubble writing.

The positive action I will do each day is...

....

....

....

BOREDOM BUSTERS

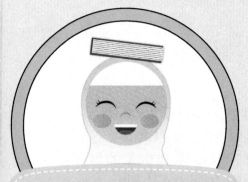

Learn to balance a book on your head and walk for 20 steps.

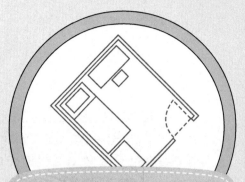

Draw and colour a map of your bedroom or classroom.

Share a story using only pictures.

Make friendship bracelets to gift to family and friends.

Make a yummy fresh fruit juice with your parent.

HOW WELL DID YOU DO TODAY?

Did you manage to do 10 good deeds? Colour in a gold coin for each good deed you did today. May Allah accept it and reward you 10 times over and more, to deposit in your Jannah Bank.

Let's reflect on how good we were today.

Thoughts and Reflections

What are you grateful for today?

....

....

What made you smile today?

....

....

What will you try to be even better at tomorrow insha Allah?

....

....

DAY 16

Did you know?

The Prophet Muhammad (peace be upon him) said: "A man follows the religion of his friend, so each one should consider whom he makes friends with."

Challenge

Tell your friends how awesome they are.

Allah is Al-Walee (The Protective Friend)

Jannah is grateful she has wonderful friends.
Write the names of all your friends.

Colour in the bubble writing.

FRIENDS

Names of my friends

1 ....

2 ....

3 ....

4 ....

5 ....

Jannah would like to make new friends. Which qualities do you think she should look for in a friend? Write one in each heart.

HOW WELL DID YOU DO TODAY?

Did you manage to do 10 good deeds? Colour in a gold coin for each good deed you did today. May Allah accept it and reward you 10 times over and more, to deposit in your Jannah Bank.

Let's reflect on how good we were today.

Thoughts and Reflections

What are you grateful for today?

....

....

What made you smile today?

....

....

What will you try to be even better at tomorrow insha Allah?

....

....

Did you know?

The Prophet Yunus was swallowed by a big whale!

Challenge

Next time you may feel angry, try to walk away and count to 10 slowly, breathing in deeply. Then say astaghfirullah.

Allah is Al Hakeem (The All-Wise)

Do you sometimes feel sad? That's OK because we all feel sad sometimes. The Prophet Yunus (pbuh) said this dua when he was in the belly of the whale.

**La ilaha illa anta, subhaa naka,
innee kuntu mina ath-thalimeen.**

(There is no deity except You, exalted are You. Indeed, I have been of the wrong-doers.)

Can you memorise this dua? Now you can say it everytime you feel sad. Jannah is learning this dua.

HOPE

Colour in the bubble writing.

Write an acrostic poem for the word HOPE

H ....

O ....

P ....

E ....

Do you know these duas?
Learn them and say them
when needed.
What to say when...

When starting to study

رَبِّ اشْرَحْ لِي صَدْرِي وَيَسِّرْ لِي أَمْرِي وَاحْلُلْ عُقْدَةً مِّن لِّسَانِي يَفْقَهُوا قَوْلِي

Rabbishrah lee sadri Wayassir lee amree Wahlul 'uqdatun min lisanee Yaf qahoo qawlee

O Allah! Expand for me my chest (with assurance). And ease for me my talk. And untie the knot from my tongue, that they may understand my speech

When getting up from a gathering

سُبْحـانَكَ اللّهُمَّ وَبِحَمدِك، أَشْهَدُ أَنْ لا إِلهَ إِلاَّ أَنْتَ أَسْتَغْفِرُكَ وَأَتوبُ إِلَيْك

Subhaanaka Allaahumma wa bihamdika, 'ash-hadu 'an laa 'ilaaha 'illaa 'Anta, 'astaghfiruka wa 'atoobu 'ilayka

Glory is to You, O Allah, and praise is to You. I bear witness that there is none worthy of worship but You. I seek Your forgiveness and repent to You

When someone does something good for me

جَزاكَ اللہُ خَـيْراً

JazaakAllaahu khayran

May Allah reward you with good

When breaking my fast

اللَّهُمَّ لَكَ صُمْتُ وَعَلَى رِزْقِكَ أَفْطَرْتُ

Allahumma inni laka sumtu wa ala rizq-ika-aftartu

O Allah! For You I have fasted and upon your provision, I have broken my fast

When feeling angry

أَعُوذُ بِاللهِ مِنَ الشَّيْطانِ الرَّجِيْم

A'oothu billaahi minash-Shaytaanir-rajeem

I seek refuge with Allah against the Satan, the outcast

HOW WELL DID YOU DO TODAY?

Did you manage to do 10 good deeds? Colour in a gold coin for each good deed you did today. May Allah accept it and reward you 10 times over and more, to deposit in your Jannah Bank.

Let's reflect on how good we were today.

Thoughts and Reflections

What are you grateful for today?

....

....

What made you smile today?

....

....

What will you try to be even better at tomorrow insha Allah?

....

....

Did you know?

The first wahi (revelation) that came down to Prophet Muhammad (peace be upon him) was "Iqra" (read)!

Challenge

Read for at least 20 minutes each day.

Allah

Angel Jibrael

Prophet Muhammad

Allah is Al-Haadi (The Guide)

Reading is so much fun and very important too. What are the titles of the books you enjoy reading? Jannah enjoys reading about Prophet Muhammad (pbuh).

Colour in the bubble writing.

IQRA

My favourite books are:

1 ....

2 ....

3 ....

4 ....

5 ....

Jannah loves to read different books. Write some book titles you would recommend to Jannah in the hearts.

HOW WELL DID YOU DO TODAY?

Did you manage to do 10 good deeds? Colour in a gold coin for each good deed you did today. May Allah accept it and reward you 10 times over and more, to deposit in your Jannah Bank.

Let's reflect on how good we were today.

Thoughts and Reflections

What are you grateful for today?

....

....

What made you smile today?

....

....

What will you try to be even better at tomorrow insha Allah?

....

....

Did you know?

The Prophet Muhammad (peace be upon him) said: "When a Muslim performs wudu (ablution), his sins are removed from his hearing, his sight, his hands, and his legs. If he sits down, he will sit down forgiven.

Bismillah!

Challenge

Do wudu now and pray 2 rakat (units) and thank Allah for all His mercy.

Allah is Al-Quddus (The Absolutely Pure)

The Quran says: "Allah intends for you ease and does not intend for you hardship." (2:185)

So in the case where you do not have any water to do wudu with, you can do tayammum. Can you write the steps of tayammum? Jannah loves to keep clean with wudu.

WUDU

Colour in the bubble writing.

1
2
3
4
5
6

Jannah wants to do wudu. Put the steps she has to do in the correct order. Use the boxes below for help.

Wash feet 3 times, including the ankles, starting with the right foot.

Make the niyyah to pray and say Bismillah.

Wash hands 3 times, starting with the right hand.

Wipe the head once over and clean ears.

Wash arms up to and including elbows 3 times, starting with the right arm.

Wash nose 3 times.

Wash face 3 times.

Wash mouth 3 times.

8 STEPS OF WUDU

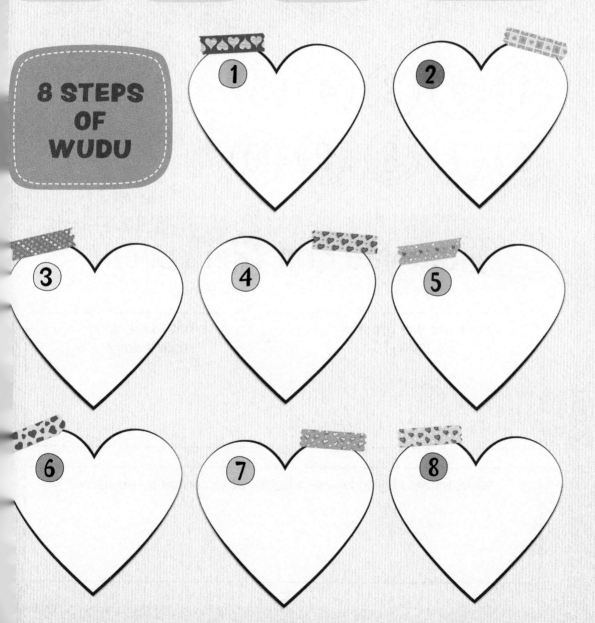

1

2

3

4

5

6

7

8

HOW WELL DID YOU DO TODAY?

Did you manage to do 10 good deeds? Colour in a gold coin for each good deed you did today. May Allah accept it and reward you 10 times over and more, to deposit in your Jannah Bank.

Let's reflect on how good we were today.

Thoughts and Reflections

What are you grateful for today?

....

....

What made you smile today?

....

....

What will you try to be even better at tomorrow insha Allah?

....

....

Did you know?

One of the most beloved deeds to Allah is praying on time.

Challenge

Make the niyyah to pray all your prayers on time.

Allah is Al-Malik (The King and Owner of Dominion)

When you are praying, remember Allah sees you even though you do not see Him. So connect with Allah in your Salah and remember to ask Al-Malik in your sujood (prostration). Jannah loves to make her 6 dream duas in sujood.

SALAH

Colour in the bubble writing.

Fill in the missing words

There are .... pillars in Islam.

Salah is the .... pillar.

Muslims have to pray .... prayers each day.

List the names of the five prayers in the order they are prayed each day.

1 ....

2 ....

3 ....

4 ....

5 ....

I am going to pray with my friends at the mosque.

I am going to pray with my baba.

I am going to pray with my sister.

Take Action!

Choose a Salah time to pray in jama'ah (congregation).

HOW WELL DID YOU DO TODAY?

Did you manage to do 10 good deeds? Colour in a gold coin for each good deed you did today.
May Allah accept it and reward you 10 times over and more, to deposit in your Jannah Bank.

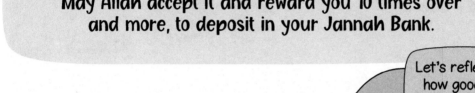

Let's reflect on how good we were today.

Thoughts and Reflections

What are you grateful for today?

....

....

What made you smile today?

....

....

What will you try to be even better at tomorrow insha Allah?

....

....

DAY 21

Did you know?

The Prophet Muhammad (peace be upon him) said: "Prayer in jama'ah (congregation) is better than prayer alone by 27 degrees."

Challenge

Pray a salah in jama'ah.

Allah is Al-Mu'min
(The One Who Gives Eman and Security)

When we pray in jama'ah this helps us to connect with one another and be stronger together insha Allah. Jannah encourages her family to pray together in jama'ah as much as possible.

Colour in the bubble writing.

JAMA'AH

Write the names of the salahs you prayed in jama'ah today.

....

....

....

....

SALAH TIMES FOR TODAY

Draw the hands on the analogue clock and write in the digital clock for each prayer time today.

1 Fajr

2 Dhuhr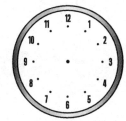

3 Asr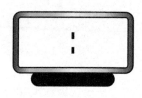

4 Maghrib

5 Isha

HOW WELL DID YOU DO TODAY?

Did you manage to do 10 good deeds? Colour in a gold coin for each good deed you did today. May Allah accept it and reward you 10 times over and more, to deposit in your Jannah Bank.

Let's reflect on how good we were today.

Thoughts and Reflections

What are you grateful for today?

....

....

What made you smile today?

....

....

What will you try to be even better at tomorrow insha Allah?

....

....

DAY 22

Did you know?

The Prophet Muhammad (peace be upon him) said: "The best charity is when a Muslim man gains knowledge then he teaches it to his Muslim brother."

Challenge

Give the charity of knowledge and share something you learnt today with your family.

Allah is Al-Aleem
(The All-Knowing, The Omniscient)

If you share a new surah you learnt with your family or friends, and then they read it in their salah, insha Allah, you get rewarded for everytime they use it. Jannah likes to teach her younger brother the Quran she learns.

ILM

Colour in the bubble writing.

What will you teach others today?

....

....

....

FIVE PILLARS OF ISLAM

Can you write the five pillars of Islam in the pillars below?

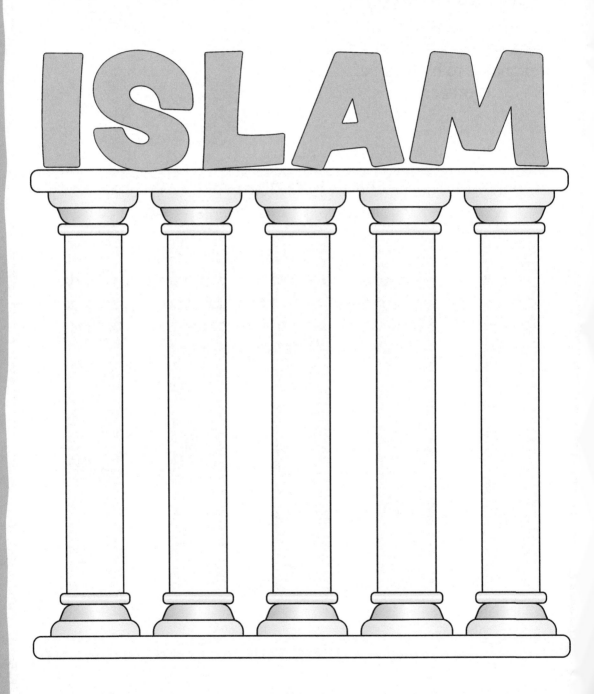

HOW WELL DID YOU DO TODAY?

Did you manage to do 10 good deeds? Colour in a gold coin for each good deed you did today. May Allah accept it and reward you 10 times over and more, to deposit in your Jannah Bank.

Let's reflect on how good we were today.

Thoughts and Reflections

What are you grateful for today?

....

....

What made you smile today?

....

....

What will you try to be even better at tomorrow insha Allah?

....

....

Did you know?

There are some types of food mentioned in the Quran.

Challenge

Can you name seven different foods mentioned in the Quran?

Allah is Al-Razaq (The All Provider)

There are many health benefits to eating the fruits mentioned in the Quran. Jannah loves eating pomegranate.

RIZQ

Colour in the bubble writing.

Draw a picture of your favourite food.

FABULOUS FOODS

Can you match the fruit to its description?

pomegranate

dates

grapes

banana

onions

garlic

I am white and used in cooking. I have many cloves.

I am fleshy, round and grow in clusters.

I am the Prophet's favourite fruit.

I am sweet and recommended to break your fast with me.

I am a vegetable and have layers.

I am yellow, long and curved.

HOW WELL DID YOU DO TODAY?

Did you manage to do 10 good deeds? Colour in a gold coin for each good deed you did today. May Allah accept it and reward you 10 times over and more, to deposit in your Jannah Bank.

Let's reflect on how good we were today.

Thoughts and Reflections

What are you grateful for today?

....

....

What made you smile today?

....

....

What will you try to be even better at tomorrow insha Allah?

....

....

DAY 24

Did you know?
There are 4 promises of Allah to humankind.

Challenge
Remember these promises and make it a habit to say lots of alhamdulillah and astaghfirullah.

Allah is Ar-Ra'oof (The Most Kind)

The four promises of Allah are:
1. If you make dua to Allah, He will respond. (40:60)
2. Allah will not punish those who ask him forgiveness (8:33)
3. If you remember Allah, He will remember you. (2:152)
4. If you are grateful, He will bless you with more. (14:07)

Colour in the bubble writing.

PROMISE

Jannah is making a promise to herself that she will always do her best.

Write a promise to yourself.

I promise ....

....

....

PRETTY PURE PROMISES

Can you think of some beautiful promises
you can make to help yourself, your family,
your friends, school or your planet?
Write or draw them below.

HOW WELL DID YOU DO TODAY?

Did you manage to do 10 good deeds? Colour in a gold coin for each good deed you did today. May Allah accept it and reward you 10 times over and more, to deposit in your Jannah Bank.

Let's reflect on how good we were today.

Thoughts and Reflections

What are you grateful for today?

....

....

What made you smile today?

....

....

What will you try to be even better at tomorrow insha Allah?

....

....

DAY 25

Did you know?

The best ayah in the Quran is called Ayatul Kursi.

Challenge

Memorise this beautiful ayah and read it after every salah.

Ayatul Kursi

Allah is Al-Fattah (The Opener)

Reading this amazing ayah can protect you from many things. Jannah likes to read it every morning when she leaves her home, and every night before going to sleep.

PROTECTION

Colour in the bubble writing.

When do you read Ayatul Kursi? Write it below.

....

....

....

AYATUL KURSI

Memorise this wonderful ayah and read it after every salah.

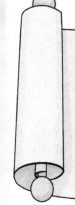

اللَّهُ لاَ إِلَهَ إِلاَّ هُوَ الْحَيُّ الْقَيُّومُ لاَ تَأْخُذُهُ سِنَةٌ وَلاَ نَوْمٌ لَهُ مَا فِي السَّمَاوَاتِ وَمَا فِي الأَرْضِ مَنْ ذَا الَّذِي يَشْفَعُ عِنْدَهُ إِلاَّ بِإِذْنِهِ يَعْلَمُ مَا بَيْنَ أَيْدِيهِمْ وَمَا خَلْفَهُمْ وَلاَ يُحِيطُونَ بِشَيْءٍ مِنْ عِلْمِهِ إِلاَّ بِمَا شَاءَ وَسِعَ كُرْسِيُّهُ السَّمَاوَاتِ وَالأَرْضَ وَلاَ يَئُودُهُ حِفْظُهُمَا وَهُوَ الْعَلِيُّ الْعَظِيمُ 2:255

Transliteration

Allahu laaa ilaaha illaa huwal haiyul qai-yoom
laa taakhuthuhoo sinatun wa laa nawm; lahoo maa fissamaawaati wa maa fil ard
man thallathee yashfa'u indahoo ilaa be ithnih
ya'lamu maa baina aideehim wa maa khalfahum
wa laa yuheetoona beshai 'immin 'ilmihee illa be maa shaaaa
wasi'a kursiyyuhus samaa waati wal arda wa la ya'ooduho hifzuhumaa
wa huwa aliyyul a'theem

English

Allah – there is no deity except Him, the Ever-Living,
the Sustainer of (all) existence.
Neither drowsiness overtakes Him nor sleep.
To Him belongs whatever is in the heavens and whatever is on the earth.
Who is it that can intercede with Him except by His permission?
He knows what is [presently] before them and what will be after them,
and they encompass not a thing of His knowledge except for what He wills.
His Kursi extends over the heavens and the earth,
and their preservation tires Him not.
And He is the Most High, the Most Great.

HOW WELL DID YOU DO TODAY?

Did you manage to do 10 good deeds? Colour in a gold coin for each good deed you did today. May Allah accept it and reward you 10 times over and more, to deposit in your Jannah Bank.

Let's reflect on how good we were today.

Thoughts and Reflections

What are you grateful for today?

....

....

What made you smile today?

....

....

What will you try to be even better at tomorrow insha Allah?

....

....

Did you know?

Allah has 99 names.

Challenge

Read the 99 names of Allah. Use different names of Allah when making dua.

Allah is Al-Wadud (The Most Loving)

Allah is kind in giving us His beautiful names, so that we may understand who He is. Jannah loves the name Al-Wadud.

LOVE

Colour in the bubble writing.

Write down some of the names of Allah that you know.

....

....

....

NAMES OF ALLAH

Can you match Allah's name to the English meaning?

Al-Fattah	The Provider
Al-Razzaq	The Ever-Giving
As-Samee	The Supreme Opener
Al-Wahhab	The All-Knowing
Al-Aleem	The All-Hearing

HOW WELL DID YOU DO TODAY?

Did you manage to do 10 good deeds? Colour in a gold coin for each good deed you did today. May Allah accept it and reward you 10 times over and more, to deposit in your Jannah Bank.

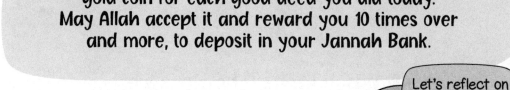

Let's reflect on how good we were today.

Thoughts and Reflections

What are you grateful for today?

....

....

What made you smile today?

....

....

What will you try to be even better at tomorrow insha Allah?

....

....

Challenge

Find the direction of the Qibla at home.

Did you know?

The Qibla is the direction that all Muslims around the world pray towards.

Allah is Al-Mu'izz (The Honourer)

Qibla is an Arabic word which means the direction Muslims face in their salah. The first direction of Qibla was facing towards Jerusalem. It was then changed to the direction of the Kaaba in Makkah. Jannah is learning how to find the Qibla using a compass.

QIBLA

Colour in the bubble writing.

Write the word Qibla in Arabic in bubble writing and colour it in.

DESIGN **YOUR PRAYER MAT**

Can you design your own prayer mat and Qibla arrow?

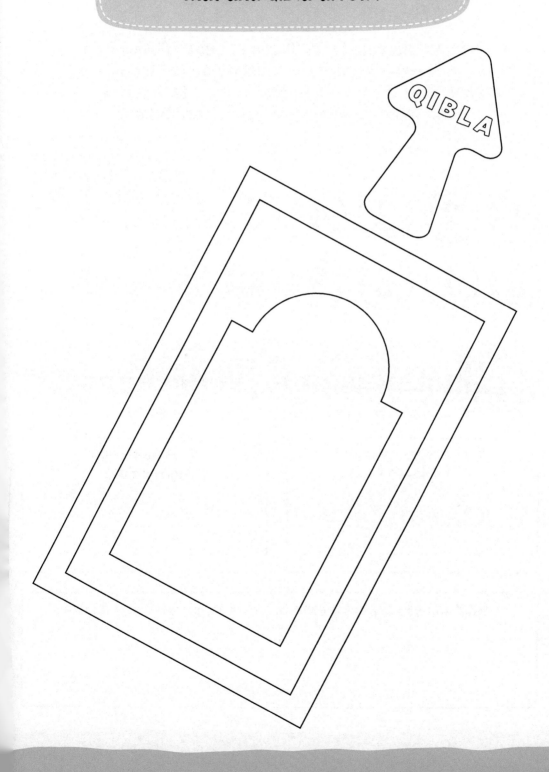

HOW WELL DID YOU DO TODAY?

Did you manage to do 10 good deeds? Colour in a gold coin for each good deed you did today. May Allah accept it and reward you 10 times over and more, to deposit in your Jannah Bank.

Let's reflect on how good we were today.

Thoughts and Reflections

What are you grateful for today?

....

....

What made you smile today?

....

....

What will you try to be even better at tomorrow insha Allah?

....

....

Did you know?

The Prophet Muhammad (peace be upon him) said: "Give sadaqa (charity) without delay, for it stands in the way of calamity."

Challenge

Give charity to the needy people in your local community and ask Allah to protect you from all harm.

Allah is Al-Qabid (The Withholder)

As Muslims we should love for others what we love for ourselves. Charity is one of the pillars of Islam and it protects you in different ways. Jannah loves to donate food to people in need.

SADAQA

Colour in the bubble writing.

Draw or list acts of sadaqa

WORD SEARCH

Can you find these words in the word search below?

☐ happy ☐ smile ☐ charity ☐ bright ☐ good

☐ hasanah ☐ blessing ☐ people ☐ Jannah ☐ Allah

H	A	S	A	N	A	H	F	M	O	V	Z	Q
S	D	L	B	U	W	B	D	C	Z	B	F	X
T	S	M	I	L	E	G	O	H	R	I	O	L
N	X	J	P	P	S	J	O	I	M	T	H	Q
U	V	G	A	V	N	S	G	T	T	B	A	S
L	F	T	R	Z	H	H	F	F	P	C	P	L
C	H	A	R	I	T	Y	R	D	E	G	P	T
C	L	D	H	U	A	Q	O	M	O	Z	Y	T
R	N	O	J	N	L	R	N	M	P	E	E	L
H	M	B	M	C	L	H	F	O	L	S	N	D
S	Z	L	I	B	A	G	N	X	E	J	F	U
J	A	N	N	A	H	D	T	K	G	N	K	I
T	N	T	D	U	G	N	I	S	S	E	L	B

HOW WELL DID YOU DO TODAY?

Did you manage to do 10 good deeds? Colour in a gold coin for each good deed you did today. May Allah accept it and reward you 10 times over and more, to deposit in your Jannah Bank.

Let's reflect on how good we were today.

Thoughts and Reflections

What are you grateful for today?

....

....

What made you smile today?

....

....

What will you try to be even better at tomorrow insha Allah?

....

....

DAY 29

Did you know?

The Prophet Muhammad (peace be upon him) said: "There is no believing servant who supplicates (dua) for his brother in his absence where the angels do not say 'The same be for you'".

Challenge

Next time you make dua, remember your brothers and sisters around the world. The angels will say: "The same be for you."

Ya Allah

Allah is Al-Baasit (The Extender)

When making dua begin by praising Allah and then sending prayers upon our beloved Prophet (pbuh). Jannah loves to raise her hands when making dua for others.

Colour in the bubble writing.

Write the duas you would like to make for others

1 ....

2 ....

3 ....

4 ....

MY DUA BOOK

Let's make a dua hands craft book and write the people you wish to make dua for.
Make sure you get an adult to help you!

What you will need

- Coloured hard paper
- Glue
- Scissors
- Colour pencils or markers

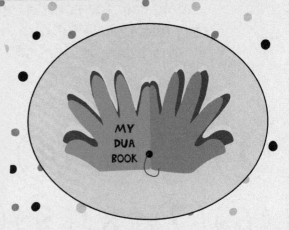

What to do

- Fold a coloured paper in half and trace your hand on the paper, with your little finger closest to the folded part.

- Cut around your hand print.

- Open your cut out hand print paper and put it onto another coloured paper. Now trace around your cut out hand print but this time leave some space around it.

- Cut out the second hand print and stick the smaller one on top of it.

- Write the names of the people you wish to make dua for.

- Decorate the card.

HOW WELL DID YOU DO TODAY?

Did you manage to do 10 good deeds? Colour in a gold coin for each good deed you did today. May Allah accept it and reward you 10 times over and more, to deposit in your Jannah Bank.

Let's reflect on how good we were today.

Thoughts and Reflections

What are you grateful for today?

....

....

What made you smile today?

....

....

What will you try to be even better at tomorrow insha Allah?

....

....

DAY 30

Did you know?

The Prophet Muhammad (peace be upon him) said:
"Take up good deeds only as much as you are able, for the best deeds are those done regularly even if they are few."

Challenge

Ask yourself, which good deed will you be able to do every day, even if it is small. Make a promise to yourself you will do this every day sincerely for Allah.

Allah is Al-Muhaymin (The Guardian)

Your actions are based on your intentions. So it is really important to have pure niyyah to please Allah alone and not show off to others.

HASANAH

Colour in the bubble writing.

Write the regular hasanah you would like to do insha Allah.

1 ....

2 ....

3 ....

4 ....

5 ....

MY GOOD DEEDS CHART

Colour in a box for each of the good deeds you have done each day. Have fun!

	MONDAY	TUESDAY	WEDNESDAY	THURSDAY	FRIDAY	SATURDAY	SUNDAY
Read Quran							
Salah							
Make dhikr							
Smile							
Help others							
Make dua							
Clean up							
Kind words							
Share							

HOW WELL DID YOU DO TODAY?

Did you manage to do 10 good deeds? Colour in a gold coin for each good deed you did today. May Allah accept it and reward you 10 times over and more, to deposit in your Jannah Bank.

Let's reflect on how good we were today.

Thoughts and Reflections

What are you grateful for today?

....

....

What made you smile today?

....

....

What will you try to be even better at tomorrow insha Allah?

....

....

WEEKLY WINS

Colour in a box for each of the good deeds you have done each day. Have fun!

	MONDAY	TUESDAY	WEDNESDAY	THURSDAY	FRIDAY	SATURDAY	SUNDAY
Read Quran							
Salah							
Make dhikr							
Smile							
Help others							
Make dua							
Clean up							
Kind words							
Share							

WEEKLY WINS

Colour in a box for each of the good deeds you have done each day. Have fun!

	MONDAY	TUESDAY	WEDNESDAY	THURSDAY	FRIDAY	SATURDAY	SUNDAY
Read Quran							
Salah							
Make dhikr							
Smile							
Help others							
Make dua							
Clean up							
Kind words							
Share							

Mabrook!

Congratulations for completing 30 days worth of good deeds!
Insha Allah you have learnt more about how Loving Allah is and
about our beloved Prophet (pbuh).

Insha Allah you have learnt lots of new ways to save rewards in
your Jannah Bank. Keep up with all the wonderful and easy ways
in choosing to be good and saving in your Jannah Bank insha Allah.

jannah bank

May your race to Jannah be easy and
highly rewarding.

Aameen.

Printed in Great Britain
by Amazon

39616095R00057